BY HELEN DOSS

A Brother the Size of Me

The Really Real Family

PICTURE BOOKS

All the Children of the World

Friends Around the World

ADULT READING

The Family Nobody Wanted

If You Adopt a Child

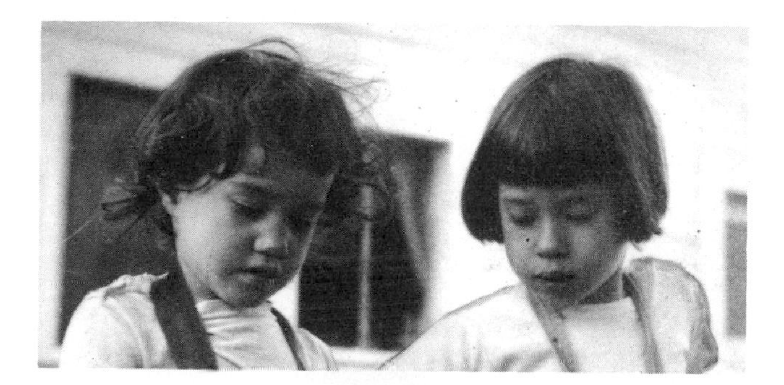

The Really Real Family

Pearn Pollinger & Higham

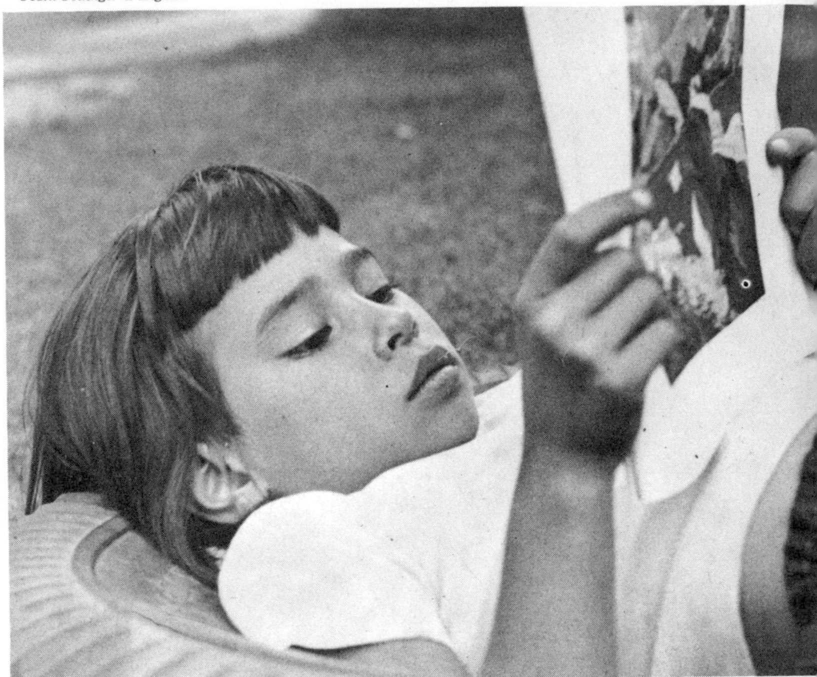

Little, Brown and Company • Boston • Toro

Miller, Magnum Photos

The REALLY REAL Family

by HELEN DOSS

LIBRARY OF CONGRESS CATALOG CARD NO. 59-5280

Second Printing

Published simultaneously in Canada
by Little, Brown & Company (Canada) Limited

PRINTED IN THE UNITED STATES OF AMERICA

Contents

The Really Real Family

James Clarke

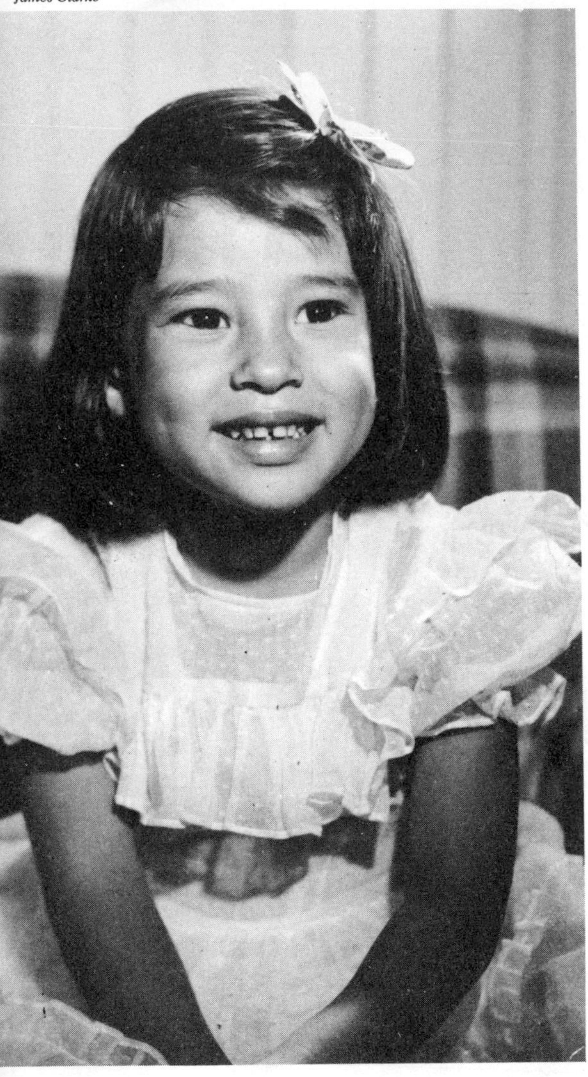

This is a picture of me, Elaine. It's the picture that man took back there in my Hawaiian house.

Chapter 1.

The Secret of the Pictures

MY NAME is Elaine. I am a real girl, and I live in California.

Once I lived a long way across the ocean in the Hawaiian Islands. I had a sister named Diane who was one year younger than

I am, and she still is. Still is my sister and one year younger, I mean.

But we didn't have any mother then, and we didn't have any daddy, and we missed not having a mother or a daddy like other children.

We lived in Honolulu, not too far from Waikiki Beach, with a nice old lady named Aunt Lulu. She wasn't really our aunt, because we didn't have any relatives. She was just taking care of Diane and me, and four little babies besides, until we could find families of our very own.

James Clarke

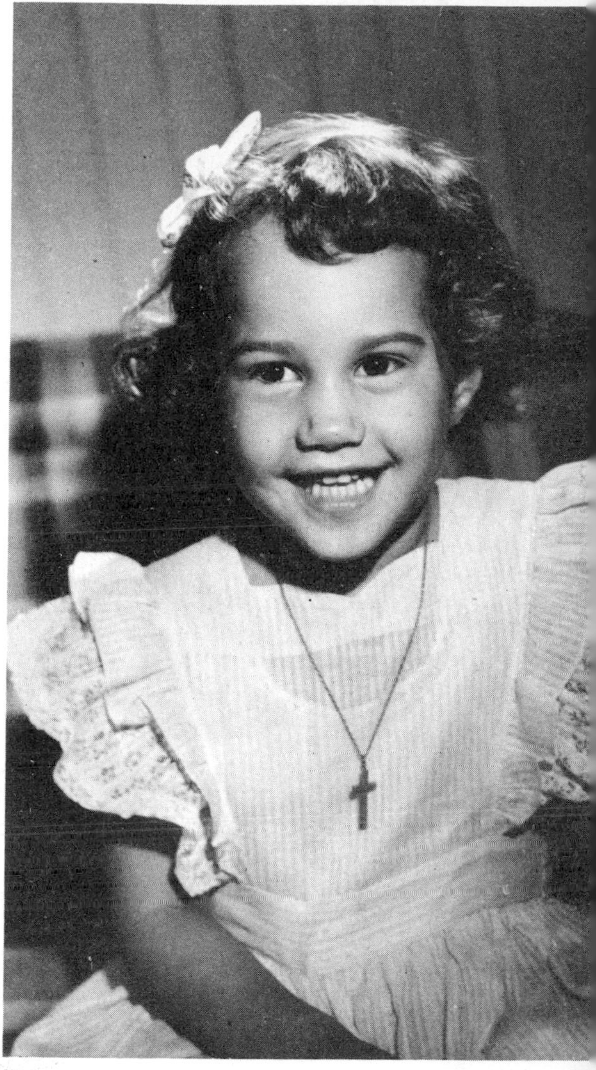

This is my younger sister, Diane. My hair is straight and hers is a little bit curly.

This was quite a while ago. But I can remember it very well, especially the day that man came to take our pictures. I remember the pictures because that was when all the secret and exciting things started to happen.

Diane and I were out in the side yard when the picture-man knocked at our front door. Diane was playing with some stick dolls under the twisted roots of the banyan tree. I was sitting by the hibiscus bush, stringing red wili-wili seeds together to make a *lei* to hang around my neck.

Here came that man knock-knocking on our door, and Aunt Lulu came bustling up to the inside of the screen. "Yes, young man?" she said through the screen.

The man had a big camera and some poles under his arm. "Is this where the two orphans from the agency live?" he asked most politely. "The ones I'm supposed to take photographs of?"

"Come in, come in," Aunt Lulu said. She held open the screen door while he went in.

In a minute Diane peeked out from behind a root

of the banyan tree. "Elaine, what are orphans?"

"We're orphans," I whispered. "That means we don't have any family. Just no family at all."

"We've got Aunt Lulu." Diane looked puzzled. After all, when you're a year younger, there are a lot of things you don't quite understand.

"She just takes care of us for the agency until the agency finds a real family for us, to adopt us," I explained.

"What does 'adopt' mean?"

I thought a minute. "Well, it's when a man and a lady want somebody to be their very own child. So they adopt him. Or her. And that means they really belong together, forever and ever."

Diane looked wistful. "Wouldn't that be nice, to have a really *real* family, all our very own?"

I thought so too, but I didn't have time to answer. Just then Aunt Lulu opened the screen door and called, "Elaine! Diane!"

We went running, and she held the door open for us.

"Come in, dears," she said, patting us on our heads.

"This nice man has come to take your pictures." She scowled at the mud on Diane's bare feet and tried to brush some of the dirt off our playsuits.

"Goodness gracious," she said to the man, "I can't have their pictures taken this way. Why, they just wouldn't show the girls off at their best!" Then she got all flustered and took our hands and started marching us back to the bedrooms.

Diane looked back at the man as she was getting dragged down the hall. "Do we have to wear *shoes* for the picture?"

The man laughed and called to Aunt Lulu. "Don't worry, their feet won't show. I'm just taking the top half."

Aunt Lulu sniffed. "Well, at least the top half will be scrubbed clean, then."

She marched us into the bathroom and told me to jump out of my playsuit. She helped Diane out of hers to hurry Diane along. Then she took a soapy washcloth and scrubbed our necks and ears and faces and hands until they felt hot, almost as if the skin had been scrubbed off.

She even scrubbed our knees. "Hey," Diane complained, "that man said he was only going to take pictures of our top half."

"I just figure a body never can tell," Aunt Lulu muttered under her breath. "Better safe than sorry, I always say."

She was drying us then, the way you'd polish an apple. As soon as I could get my face out of the towel, I said, "Why is that man taking our pictures, Aunt Lulu?"

"No time to talk *now*," she said, and whisked us down the hall into our little bedroom. Diane and I slept in one room, and the four little babies Aunt Lulu took care of had their four cribs in the big front bedroom.

Aunt Lulu pulled our ruffly petticoats down over our heads and our white ruffly Sunday drcsses. I started buttoning up Diane's back buttons, and at the same time Aunt Lulu was buttoning up my back buttons.

"We don't have to wear shoes, do we?" Diane asked again. She hardly ever liked to wear shoes.

Wayne Miller, Magnum Photos

For that matter, neither did I. It was so much nicer to go barefoot.

Aunt Lulu combed back our hair and pinned on some ribbon bows. "No, I guess we'd better not keep the poor man waiting any longer, and he said your feet wouldn't show. Now *wiki-wiki,* back to the living room."

Wiki-wiki is a Hawaiian word meaning "quick," so we scooted back in a hurry.

The strange young man was standing in the living room, waiting for us. He smiled and waved toward the couch. "If you young ladies will hop up there, I'll take your pictures."

He had his camera set up on three-legged stilts, and it was pointed right at us. He leaned over and peered through his glasses right into the camera.

"My, my, such solemn little faces!" He pointed his camera right at Diane. "Little girl, do you know anyone who can wiggle his ears?"

Diane shook her head, puzzled. "No."

He held up his hand. "Now watch me very close," he said. "Just watch my ears."

I tied Diane's sash for her and helped her with her back buttons.

We both watched, and slowly his ears started to wiggle. They wiggled and made his glasses jiggle on his nose. Diane laughed out loud, and the man snapped the picture.

Then he pointed his camera right at me, and he wiggled his ears once more. I laughed again.

"I think these will turn out just fine," he said.

"Can we take off our Sunday dresses now, me and Elaine," Diane asked, "and go out to play?"

"And now are you going to tell us what the pictures are for?" I asked. I was very curious, because Aunt Lulu had acted so funny when I asked her before.

"No, Elaine, not now," Aunt Lulu said, patting my head. "You may both run and put your play clothes back on, and be sure to hang your dresses up again."

I didn't want to give up, because I was so curious. "Is it a secret?" I asked. "About the pictures, I mean."

"Well, now, Elaine," she said, looking all flustered again. "I guess you *would* call it a sort of a secret, yes."

So we ran on down the hall to the bedrooms.

"Pretty little things," I heard the man tell Aunt

Lulu. "That one you called Elaine looks part Japanese, like me. But the one with the curly hair looks a bit more Hawaiian."

"They are typical Island children," I heard Aunt Lulu say. "A beautiful blend of races and nationalities, God bless 'em." Then the front screen door banged as they went outside, and we couldn't hear them.

"Elaine, what are they talking about?" Diane asked me as I helped unbutton her back buttons. "Is it about the secret?"

"Could be," I whispered. "Do you know what I think? I think maybe somebody is wanting to adopt us."

"How do you know?" Diane asked, helping me with my back buttons.

"I don't, because I'm just guessing. But do you remember Sonny, that boy with the yellow hair and the big blue eyes? You know, the one Aunt Lulu took care of last summer for the agency."

Diane nodded.

"And do you remember when the agency lady called up Aunt Lulu and talked to her a long time on the phone, and the potatoes burned? And then, right after that, a man came and took Sonny's picture."

"Not this same man," Diane said. "The other man couldn't wiggle his ears."

"I know, but a man *did* come and take Sonny's picture, right on that very same couch." I looked Diane straight in the eye. "And do you remember what happened, *that very next week?*"

Diane nodded, and her eyes grew big. "Sonny got a new mama and a daddy! Was he an orphan too, like us?"

"Just like us," I told her. "And right after he had his picture taken, he got adopted. Right that very next week, here came the agency lady, and she brought this great big man with the yellow hair and the pretty lady with the blue eyes."

"I remember," Diane said wistfully. "They took Sonny away with them, and he's going to be their boy forever and ever."

I had my play suit on again, but I wasn't ready to go outside yet. I sat on the floor, thinking.

I was remembering the way the man shook hands

with Sonny, and threw him up into the air. And the way the pretty lady hugged him, looking all mixed up, sad and happy, because she was laughing and had tears in her eyes at the same time.

And then I remembered the way she looked up at the agency lady and said, "He's even more lovable than his picture!" And then she said, "I'm so glad he has yellow hair and blue eyes like us."

When I remembered this, I began to worry.

"What if," I told Diane, "somebody thinks they want to adopt two little girls. And then what if they see our pictures and they see we have dark eyes and dark hair!"

"Isn't that good?" Diane asked. "To have brown eyes and brown hair, I mean?"

"I always thought it was," I said slowly. "But what if other people are like the man and lady who took Sonny? What if they really want children with yellow hair and blue eyes?"

Diane looked sad, the way that I felt right then. "Then I guess they wouldn't want us," she said.

We didn't get to go out and play after all.

Aunt Lulu called us to help give the babies their bottles. After that it was time to help scrub the vegetables for supper, and to set the table. But all the time I helped Aunt Lulu, I kept wondering about those pictures the man took of us. I wondered if pretty soon a man and a lady would be looking at the pictures and if they would decide to adopt us.

Or maybe they would not want us because we had dark eyes and dark hair.

All that next week I kept thinking about it, and I could tell that Diane was thinking about it, too. But every time I tried to ask Aunt Lulu if we were going to get adopted she just said, "I told you to hush about that, child. Of *course* you'll be adopted someday, when somebody finds out how nice you are." But I could tell she was keeping some kind of a secret.

One day I watched the man next door planing down a long plank of wood in his back yard. He let me take some of the yellow, curly shavings home to play with.

I took them into the bedroom, and Diane and I looked into the mirror while we held the shavings up around our faces like curls.

"Do you think that somebody would adopt us quicker," Diane asked, "if we had yellow curls like this?"

"I was just wondering." I sighed then and threw all my shavings into the wastebasket. "But we *don't* have yellow curls, and maybe we'll never get adopted like Sonny did." I was getting discouraged because it had been a long time and nothing had happened.

Then suddenly everything happened at once.

The telephone rang, and Aunt Lulu listened for a long time, and when she talked she grew quite excited. When she hung up, she called, "Elaine, Diane! Come, *wiki-wiki.*"

So we came running as fast as we could, all out of breath. Even though

Wayne Miller, Magnum Photos

We came running as fast as we could, all out of breath.

she hadn't been running, Aunt Lulu looked all flustered and out of breath, too.

"The lady from the agency will be here in less than an hour," she told us. Her face looked quite pink with excitement. "My house is a mess, all tracked up and baby toys strewed about. You girls clean up your room, and the nursery, *wiki-wiki,* while I tidy up in here and mop the floors."

"Is somebody going to adopt — " I began. Then I couldn't say any more. It seemed too much to hope for, that maybe now we might have a really real family of our own.

"No time for questions now, young lady," Aunt Lulu said, throwing rag dolls and balls into the playpen in the corner of the living room. She bustled out to the kitchen. "You can put your questions to the lady from the agency when she arrives."

Diane and I went into the nursery and picked up the rattles and the teething rings and the other toys from the floor, and tossed them into the toy box under the window. We straightened the babies' beds, and I got a damp washcloth out of the bathroom and wiped all four little faces. The four babies goo-gooed and tried to get us to stay and play with them, but I knew Aunt Lulu was in a hurry. So I took Diane back to our room to get it clean, too.

We each straightened our own bed and then we cleaned off our dresser. Diane had torn up some paper into little bits by her bed, so I went into the kitchen to get a broom.

Aunt Lulu had the mop and pail out, and was mopping all the muddy footprints off the floor. All morning Diane had been chasing a toad around the banyan tree and under the bushes, trying to catch him for a pet. She kept pattering through the mud puddle by the dripping faucet, and she tracked mud through the house every time she went in and out, but she never caught her toad.

Aunt Lulu was beginning to perspire, trying to mop the floor so fast, and she stopped to wipe off her face.

"Elaine," she said, "you and Diane put on your clean dresses as soon as you get your room tidied, and mind you both wash up good first." She started mopping again. "When you're dressed and ready, you can wait on the front porch until the floors get dry. By then the lady from the agency should be here."

I took the broom into our bedroom and began sweeping. I told Diane to wash up good and then put on her clean dress and wait on the front porch.

Before I finished the room, Diane had put on her clean dress and gone outside. I don't think she scrubbed too well, but I didn't have time to see because I wasn't ready yet myself. Besides, I was too busy wondering what secret the agency lady might have to tell us when she came.

When the floor was swept, I had to take Diane's bed apart and make it over again. Diane always kept all her favorite things in her bed, and there they were—her old raggedy doll and some torn books and a box of stubby crayons and four balls, all making bumps under her covers.

I had just washed up and was doing the front buttons on my clean dress when I heard the front screen door bang, and running feet, and Diane shouting, "Hey, Elaine!"

There was a loud thumpety-bump, and some more scrambling, and I heard Aunt Lulu scolding Diane.

When I went into the living room, there were muddy tracks all over Aunt Lulu's clean, wet floor. Diane was sprawled across the floor, her clean dress all covered with splotches of mud. Her hands and bare feet were muddy, too. And hopping right out through the clean kitchen was a big, fat toad.

"Get that ugly *bufa* out of my house!" Aunt Lulu was commanding in a high, quavery voice.

Bufa is a Hawaiian name for toad, and Aunt Lulu couldn't stand the things. She didn't even like them outside, although she knew they were useful and ate centipedes and harmful bugs out in the garden.

I ran out into the kitchen, past the hop-hopping toad, and held the screen door open. Diane picked herself up and came scrambling on her hands and knees, trying to catch him. But the toad just hip-hopped right out the open back door, and he disappeared under the house.

Diane stood up and started pulling my hair, so I started pulling hers just as hard.

Wayne Miller, Magnum Photos

"I hate you!" she shouted. "You let my pet *bufa* go!"

"I hate you!" she shouted. "You let my pet *bufa* go!"

Aunt Lulu came and separated us then.

"Stop that fighting, Elaine," she told me. "And that's no way to talk to your sister," she told Diane. Then she gave Diane a good whack right where she sits down, and marched her back to the bathroom to get scrubbed up.

When they came back Diane was clean and had on another dress, but she was still pouting. "I don't see what I did wrong," she said. "I just had a good chance to catch my *bufa*, and I wanted to bring him in to show Elaine, and then I stumbled and he got away — "

Aunt Lulu stood there looking at her, shaking her head. Suddenly she picked Diane up and plopped her on a chair. She marched right to her bedroom, and came back with her house slippers. Diane's feet were sticking out in front of her, and they were clean for once. Aunt Lulu just hooked one of her slippers on each of Diane's feet, and shook her finger in Diane's face.

"Now you listen to me," she said, "and I'll tell you something that will help you to get along better with people, and maybe understand them when they get angry with you."

"What?" Diane was still pouting.

"There's an old saying: *If you have an argument with somebody, try stepping into his shoes for a while.*"

"I've got your shoes on," Diane said. "How does that help?"

Aunt Lulu marched out to the kitchen, filled up the bucket, and brought it back with the mop. "Now you just watch me, and all the time I'm doing this extra work, you pretend you are me. Pretend that *you* are in *my* shoes." She wrung out the mop and started mopping up all the muddy tracks. "You think how you would feel if you had your house all nice and clean for company and then a little girl muddies it all up at the last minute. And then maybe it will help you to understand why I was angry with you."

Diane wiggled her toes around in the big house slippers. "Well, if I had on your shoes, and a little girl got my clean house all muddy, I guess I'd spank her, I guess."

I was thinking about what Aunt Lulu had said, too. "If I put myself into Diane's bare feet," I said, "I guess I'd think I had a right to get mad at somebody named Elaine because that busybody named Elaine opened the kitchen door and let Diane's *bufa* out." I sighed and looked at Aunt Lulu. "I guess I should have helped catch it, and put it in a box for Diane, and *then* taken it outside."

Aunt Lulu shivered at the thought, but she smiled then. "I think you have the idea, Elaine, anyway." She leaned on the mop a minute. "If you ever have a fight with anyone and you want to understand how the other person feels about it, you just remember what I said about stepping into his shoes for a while."

"What if I'm fighting with someone smaller than me," Diane said, "and my feet won't squeeze in his shoes?"

Aunt Lulu was finishing the mopping. "It's just the *idea,*" she said. "You only need to pretend — "

There was the sound of car wheels on the gravel outside. Aunt Lulu grabbed up the mop and bucket and scurried out to the kitchen with them. Then she came back and took her house slippers off Diane, and pushed the slippers under the couch.

"And now," Aunt Lulu said, as she smoothed her apron on the way to the front door, "you girls will learn the secret of your new pictures!"

Chapter 2. A Really Real Family

THE LADY from the agency was nice, and we liked to have her come visit us. She never baby-talked to us the way some grownups did. She just made us feel that we were her friends.

She sat down on the couch with her zippered note-book on her lap. Diane and I crowded up to both sides of her.

She beamed at us, looking very happy. "Have you girls been told the wonderful news?"

"I thought I'd let you tell them about their new family," Aunt Lulu said from her rocking chair.

Diane clapped her hands. "A really *real* family, all our very own?"

"Is it true?" I asked. "Are we really going to have our own daddy and a mama?"

"Yes," the lady said, smiling. "And very soon, too."

"Did they see our pictures?" I asked. "Do they like the way we look?"

The lady laughed. "Yes, they saw your pictures, and they were just delighted with you! They quickly wrote back, air mail and special delivery, and said that they are very eager to adopt both of you girls."

I was sitting there feeling really happy inside. Diane asked, "Will Elaine and me still be sisters?"

The lady laughed again. "Yes, and that is not all. You will both get three *more* new sisters, and *four* new brothers. So what do you think of that?"

"Goody," Diane said, and I thought that would be pretty nice, too.

The lady unzippered her notebook and took out some pictures. "Now would you girls like to see some photographs of your new family?"

We leaned over to look.

"Is that going to be our new mama?" Diane asked shyly.

"Yes, there she is with your three new sisters." The lady pulled out another picture. "Here they are again with the rest of the family. The sisters are just about your same ages, too, so you'll have lots of company. This one with the yellow hair is Susie. This one with the black hair is Rita. And this chubby one is Laura."

". . . There she is with your three new sisters."

"But our new daddy doesn't have very much hair!" Diane said.

"Many men are bald these days," the lady said, smiling. "I think he has a very kind face, don't you?"

I pointed to the boys. "What names do our new brothers have?"

She studied the letter she had, and then she picked them out. "This oldest boy, with the yellow hair, is Donny. He's about three years older than you are, Elaine. This dark-haired boy is Teddy, and the mother writes that he is exactly the same age as you. And this merry-faced little Timmy, here, is a year younger than Diane. The youngest is this little Oriental toddler. His name is Alex."

"What's Oriental?" I asked.

"And what's a toddler?" Diane wanted to know.

"But our new daddy doesn't have very much hair!"

"You girls are part Oriental, Elaine," she told us. "That is like Chinese, Japanese, Korean, and such. It is the Oriental in you that gives you your lovely eyes." She pointed to the pictures again. "All of the children in this new family of yours were adopted. And many of them are part Oriental, too." She looked at Diane. "And a toddler is a child who is growing out of babyhood and learning to walk."

"Where are we going to live?" I asked.

"Over on the mainland," she said. "In California."

"Is that very far?" Diane asked.

"Goodness gracious," Aunt Lulu said, rocking back and forth. "It certainly is. It's clear across the ocean."

I wanted to know how we would get there. The agency lady explained that people could either take nearly a week to go by boat, or they could go in a day by airplane.

"We thought it would be easier for you to make the trip by airplane," she said. "We're making arrangements for you to leave Honolulu next Saturday morning early. And your new family will meet you that night at the airport in San Francisco."

Diane took the lady's hand. "Who will go on the airplane with us? Will you?"

The lady hugged her. "No, sweetie. I'll take you and Elaine to the airport. A very nice lady who is called a stewardess will take care of you on the plane until you get off and meet your new mother and daddy. And from then on, *they* will be the ones who will always love you and take care of you."

We had to look at the pictures again and again, and talk about our new family. Then the agency lady looked at her watch.

"Time for me to be going," she said. "This will be a busy time for you, until Saturday."

"What are we going to do?" Diane asked.

"Tomorrow I am going to take you downtown, and we're going to do some shopping." She stood up and zippered her notebook shut. "So I'll see you in the morning."

We were all dressed and ready, with our shoes on, when she came back the next morning.

Oh, but that was an exciting day!

We went downtown to a big department store.

We rode up on the escalator to the floor where they had children's things. First we each got a brand-new coat for the trip. Diane got a pretty green one with a big collar. Mine was just exactly like it, only blue.

Then we went to the beauty parlor, and got haircuts. Mine was cut short, with bangs.

Next, at the shoe department, we each got a pair of patent leather slippers. I didn't know that new shoes could be so pretty. They were black and so shiny you could almost see your face in them.

After that we went to a restaurant for lunch. We had hot chicken pie and crunchy rolls with jelly, and there was a special dessert — coconut ice, served in halves of coconut shells!

The biggest surprise came just before we went home. The agency lady bought Diane and me each a new doll to take to our new home.

We hugged our new dolls all the way back to Aunt Lulu's house, and we took them to bed with us.

"Pinch me," I told Diane when the lights were out. "I want to know if I'm having a good dream or if this is all real."

She reached over in the dark and pinched me then. She pinched so hard I pinched her back, and she squealed. Then we started throwing pillows at each other until Aunt Lulu put her head in the door and scolded. We were almost too excited to go to sleep that night.

The most exciting day of all, though, was the day before we left.

Aunt Lulu decided to let us celebrate our good fortune with a *luau*, which is an old-time Hawaiian feast.

For the party, Diane and I picked a big basket of yellow ginger blossoms while the early morning dew was still on them. We strung them together to make *leis*, enough for everybody, so that all the guests could wear them around their necks.

We set the table for the *luau* outside, right on the ground, the way the Hawaiians used to do. For the tablecloth we laid big, flat, green banana leaves in a long row across the grass, and we decorated it with red hibiscus flowers.

All the way down the tablecloth, we arranged fresh

fruit. In the middle was a ripe pineapple with spears of green leaves sprouting out of the top. We also had two orange papaya melons, some coconuts and yellow bananas, and some ripe mangoes.

The lady and man who lived next door came over to our *luau,* and their two big girls and their big boy were invited, too. The two girls played the ukelele and sang songs while we were getting the food ready to serve. The boy had some long, tough leaves, which he was weaving into a Hawaiian hat for us.

The lady next door brought us each a bright, flowered *muu-muu,* which she made on her sewing machine for us. A *muu-muu* is a Hawaiian dress which comes down to the ankles, with ruffles around the bottom and the armholes. Diane and I ran into the house and put ours on, and they just fit.

The lady also brought a bowl full of homemade *poi.* It had taken her several days to make it, with all the boiling and pounding and grinding up of the taro roots. It was gooey, like pale pink flour paste, and it tasted kind of pasty, too.

"The old-time Hawaiians used to eat *poi* for a main dish," Aunt Lulu told us, "just the way we eat bread or potatoes with almost every meal."

Aunt Lulu carried out from the kitchen a platter of good-smelling roast pork and another platter with a fish baked whole. Diane and I carried out two wooden bowls full of hot yams and sweet potatoes, baked in their skins.

The most fun was getting to eat everything with our fingers, just the way the Hawaiian people used to do. We even ate the gooey *poi* out of our bowls with our fingers. We would stick two fingers into the *poi*, swirl them around until a gob of *poi* clung to them, then quickly put our fingers into our mouths before we dribbled any.

The roast pork was delicious, especially the crisp, crackly part on the outside. We licked our fingers after every bite.

"Now, if we had been real old-time Hawaiians," Aunt Lulu said, "we'd have roasted our pork and our fish and sweet potatoes in an *imu*."

"What's an *imu*?" Diane asked.

"It is an underground oven," Aunt Lulu said. "You dig a big hole, and heat a lot of stones in a big fire. Then you line the hole with hot stones. And you take a whole pig, stuff it with hot stones, and put it in the middle of your *imu.* Then you wrap fish and yams and sweet potatoes and bananas in wet green leaves, and tuck all these little packages in around the pig."

"How does it cook?" Diane asked.

"Hot stones underneath," Aunt Lulu said, "and more piled on top. Then plenty of wet leaves, to make steam, and the whole thing is covered over with dirt to keep the heat inside, until everything is baked."

"It tastes mighty good this way," I told Aunt Lulu, "baked in our kitchen stove *imu.*"

The four babies were there, too. One was propped up in the baby buggy, two were sitting in the playpen, and one was bouncing in the jumper. Aunt Lulu let us feed the babies some of the fish, all chopped up, and some mashed sweet potatoes and yams. They each had a ripe banana for dessert.

I had a slice of orange papaya melon and a mango for my dessert, and then I couldn't eat any more. Everybody was stuffed by the end of our *luau!*

The girls from next door played the ukelele again, and everybody sang some more songs.

Then the girls had a surprise for us. They sang a song they made up about Diane and me going away. The youngest girl did a *hula* with the song. A *hula* is a Hawaiian dance that tells a story. The feet hardly move at all; mostly it is the hands that move very gracefully and act out the story.

This is the *hula* song they sang and danced:

Good-by to Diane,
Good-by to Elaine,
They are flying away
In a giant airplane.

They'll fly over the seas,
The breakers, the foam,
To a faraway land
Where they'll find a new home.

Everybody clapped and made them do it all over again. Then they asked Diane and me if we would dance, too.

So the girl from next door played on her ukelele, and Diane and I did "Lovely Hula Hands," which they taught us once. In our new Hawaiian *muu-muus* we danced, with our ginger blossom *leis* around our necks.

Everybody clapped for us, too. Even some of the babies laughed and clapped their fat little hands. It was a very happy day, our last day in Hawaii.

The next morning we woke up even before it was light.

When Aunt Lulu came to call us, we were already dressed in our Sunday dresses and our shiny new shoes. We didn't want to miss the airplane that was going to take us to our new daddy and mama. We just didn't want to take any chances.

We were eating cornflakes and milk when the agency lady drove up. While she put our suitcase in the car, we hurried and finished our breakfast. Then we kissed and hugged Aunt Lulu good-by and jumped into the car. At last we were off to the airport, on our way to our strange new home.

It was a big, big plane that we were going to fly in. The agency lady took us to a pretty lady in a uniform. She was the stewardess who was going to take care of us on the trip.

Then we hugged and kissed the agency lady good-by, too, and the stewardess took us up the stairs into the airplane, and showed us to our seats.

"Now, Elaine and Diane," she said, "I'll fasten your seat belts for you until the plane is on its way. I know you girls are going to enjoy your trip."

The airplane shivered when the motors started. After a while we were moving along the ground, faster and faster. We could see the agency lady waving good-by, way behind us.

Faster and faster we went. Then we started lifting up. Up and up we went until everything got smaller and smaller down below. All the people looked like ants, and the cars looked like tiny toys. We could see the waves pounding a white border along Waikiki

Beach, but they didn't look high and rough now, the way they do when you try to swim in them. The ocean looked smooth, like pretty blue glass.

We flew and flew.

For all the rest of the day, all we could see out of the windows was sky and water. Nothing but blue sky and ocean, just as far as we could see. I never knew until then that there was so much water in all the world.

At noon, when the sun was out of sight over our heads, the stewardess brought us our lunch. It was on a tray, so we could eat right in our seats. We had meat and potatoes and salad. Our milk we could drink with a straw. For dessert we had ice cream and a cookie.

"I wish we could eat everything with our fingers again, like last night," Diane said. "Wasn't that fun, Elaine?"

But I told her we had better not, even if it was fun.

After the stewardess took our trays away, we both fell asleep. I guess we were pretty sleepy from getting up so early that morning.

When we woke up, I took a comb from our little bag, and Diane and I went down the aisle to the ladies' washroom to wash up and comb our hair.

When we got back to our seats, we weren't interested in looking out of the window any more. There wasn't one little bit of land anywhere, and we were tired of looking at just sky and water.

Lots of the other passengers talked to us. All of them were very friendly, except for the grouchy man right across the aisle. He was trying to read a book, and Diane kept asking him questions. Sometimes she accidentally bumped him when she was going up and down the aisle.

The last time she bumped him, he got red in the face, and his eyebrows came together crossly.

"Listen here, little girl," he grumbled, and he banged his book shut. "Why don't you just run outside and play?"

Diane looked out of the window, her eyes big. She looked puzzled. Then she giggled. "Oh, you're teasing me. How can I, when I don't have any wings?"

The man just scowled and opened his book again. "At the rate you're going, you are not about to sprout any."

Diane climbed back into her seat. "Wouldn't that be nice, Elaine, if we could?"

"Could what?"

"Could sprout wings," Diane said dreamily. "I think I'd like to be a bird."

I sighed. "Oh, I don't know. I'm getting pretty tired of flying by now. I wish we would get there. I'm so anxious to see our new family."

"Me, too," Diane said. "Are you scared?"

"A little bit," I admitted. I couldn't help thinking, *What if they don't like us?* I made up my mind that I was going to do everything I could, when I got to my new home, to make my new family like me. I wanted to live in my new home forever and ever, until I was grown up.

At last the sun came down out of the sky, and disappeared behind the water. The sky was full of orange and pink and rosy red colors. The sky grew darker, and the colors faded to gold and lemon yellow, and then to pale, pale green. Finally the whole sky was like black velvet all sparkled with diamonds.

Diane and I kept looking at the stars for a while. Then we fell asleep again, and when we woke up, the stewardess was fastening our safety belts.

"We are landing now, girls," she smiled. "Pretty soon you'll be going home with your new family!"

All the people were combing their hair and fixing their hats and looking for their handbags. We looked out of our window and there were lots of lights down below, and they kept getting closer.

Finally our airplane settled gently on the ground. I took Diane's hand, and we went to the door of the airplane. The big steps had been pushed up to the door, and we started down.

When we reached the ground, a lady with brown hair and blue eyes rushed up to us.

"Are you Elaine and Diane?" she asked. She sat down on her heels, so she would be down where we could see her.

"I'm Elaine," I said, "and this is my little sister, Diane. Are you our new mama?"

She put her arms around me and hugged me, and said yes, she was our mama. Then she hugged Diane, and kissed us both. She was all mixed up, sad and happy, because she had tears in her eyes and she was laughing at the same time.

"I recognized you right away from your pictures," she said, kissing and hugging us all over again. "Would you like to meet your new sisters?"

I was too shy to talk any more, so I just nodded. Our new mama stepped to one side, and there were three girls behind her. One had black hair and black eyes. One had yellow wavy hair and blue eyes. And one was very pretty, with a chubby round face, and brown hair and brown eyes like Diane and me. They were all very pretty, and I liked these new sisters.

Our new mother put her hand on the girl with the black hair. "This is Rita. She is the same age as you, Diane."

She put her hand on the girl with the yellow hair. "This is Susie. She is the same age as you, Elaine."

Then she put her hand on the girl with the chubby

round face. "And this is Laura. She is also the same age as you, Elaine."

I found my tongue. "Hi, my name is Elaine," I told the girls. "And this is Diane."

Then we just stood there, each of us looking at the others and wondering what the other new ones were really like.

While we were all looking, a man with a nice face and very little hair came up. He had a baby boy in his arms and a little boy riding on his shoulders. Two bigger boys were tagging along beside him.

"Did you and the boys get our car parked?" the new mama asked. "See, our two new girls have arrived already!" She put her hand on my head. "This is Elaine, and this other one is our Diane." Then she turned to us. "Girls, this is your new daddy, and these are your new brothers."

"That's a lot of brothers," Diane said.

"A fine lot of brothers, too," our new daddy said. He handed the baby to our new mama. "This youngest brother is Alex. He is just learning how to walk and talk." Then he lifted down the boy who had been riding on his shoulders. "And this one is Timmy. He is a year younger than you, Diane."

The boy holding our new daddy's hand was just about exactly the same size as me. He had a brown face, and big brown eyes full of mischief. "I'm Teddy," he said.

Then a bigger boy with blue eyes and yellow hair walked right up and shook my hand. "Hi, Elaine — you are Elaine, aren't you? I'm Donny." Then he shook Diane's hand. "Hi, Diane. I'm Donny. Welcome to the family."

Just then I saw the stewardess behind me, smiling, and some of the passengers who were our friends.

"Look," I shouted happily. "We've got a daddy *and* a mama now!"

"Plenty sisters," Diane laughed. "Plenty brothers!"

"Plenty sisters . . . Plenty brothers!"

Chapter 3. The Jealous Sister

IT WAS too late to unpack our suitcase the first night we were in our new home. Mama gave Diane and me each some pajamas, and tucked us into bed.

Sunday morning, after breakfast, Mama helped us unpack before we went to Sunday school. There was another box, too, that the agency lady had put in with our luggage. It had a card on it, addressed to our mother.

There were flower *leis* for everybody.

Mama opened the box, and it was full of sweetly fragrant Hawaiian flowers. There were lavender orchids, which Mama pinned in her hair. And there were flower *leis* for Mama and Daddy, and all of us children. Mother let us wear our *leis* to church. Daddy was the preacher, and he wore his *lei* in the pulpit while he preached the sermon.

Right from the beginning, we liked it at our new house.

Mama and Daddy and the boys all had their rooms

on the first floor. Diane and I had a little blue-papered bedroom on the second floor. Our three new sisters had the other bedroom upstairs, on the other side of the bathroom.

The church where Daddy was the minister was right next door to our house. It was out in the country, and there were tall mountains near us, and lots of trees and flowers.

We had a big play-yard behind the church, with bicycles and wagons to play with. There was an extra big tree, too, with a treehouse in it. A big, wide rope ladder hung down from the tree. You could swing back and forth on that rope ladder, or you could climb up to the treehouse on it.

And we had a red cocker spaniel named Rufus. It was all very nice. A really real family, all our very own!

We all used to play on the big rope swing that hung from our biggest tree. We had a treehouse at the top and we used the swing for a ladder, too.

It didn't take us long to learn to tell our new sisters apart. Rita was the one with the black hair and the black eyes, and she was a tomboy. She'd rather wear jeans to play in, and she didn't care anything about dressing up in dresses. She was always catching bugs and snails and things for pets. She and Diane played together all the time, and they got along fine.

Susie was the blue-eyed one with the yellow hair. She and I became pals right away. We played dolls together. I let her play with my new doll and my Hawaiian hat, and she let me play with her dollhouse and all the teensy tiny furniture. I liked Susie.

And Laura certainly wasn't hard to remember, because I didn't get along with her *at all.*

The boys were all nice. At first I kept getting Teddy and Timmy mixed up. Donny I could remember, because he was bigger than all of us. And Alex I could remember, because he was the littlest and almost a baby. But I kept getting the names mixed for the middle two boys.

Finally I got so I could remember which one was Teddy, because he was slimmer and taller than

Timmy, and also because Teddy was just the same age as I was. Timmy was more roly-poly and chubby, and he had a deep, merry chuckle when he laughed.

Everything would have been just about perfect if it had not been for Laura. She kept picking fights with Diane and me – but mostly with me, because Diane usually was outside with Rita hunting for bugs and frogs for pets.

Wayne Miller, Magnum Photos

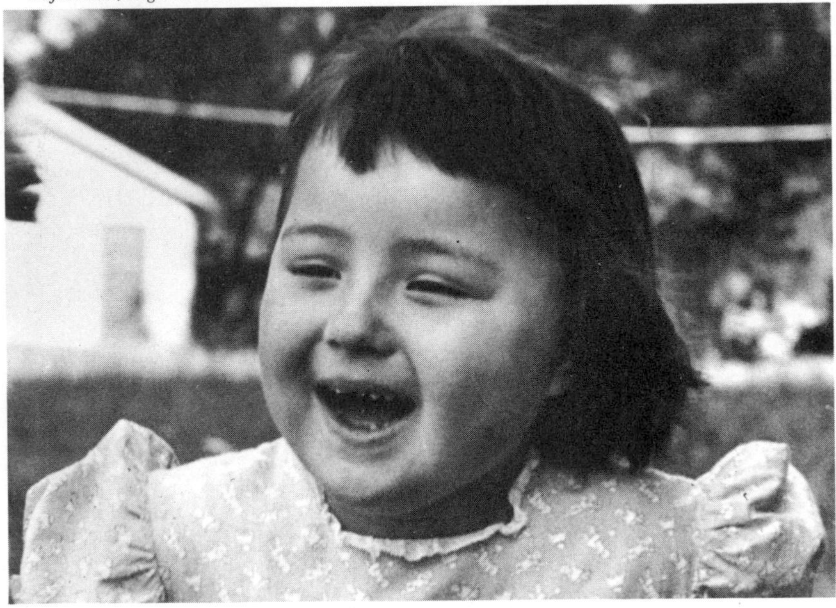

This is Laura. I thought we would never get along!

Laura wouldn't go near Diane's and Rita's pets. She wasn't a tomboy. She liked to do things in the house, and pretend she was a grown-up lady. She liked to dress up in her Sunday dresses, and comb her hair and put ribbons in it, and she liked to fancy up her room and play with her dolls.

Diane got along fine with everybody.

But when Laura had a tea party with her dolls, she wouldn't let me and my new doll come.

"You just go away," she told me, just as snooty as you please. "Nobody wants you in this house."

That hurt my feelings and made me cry. I ran to Mama and told her what Laura said.

Mama took me on her lap, wiped away my tears and kissed me. "Of course we want you in this house, Elaine. We all want you, even Laura. But Laura is just a little jealous now. She'll get over it."

"I'll bet she won't," I sniffled. "She's always trying to start a fight with me."

Mama kissed me again and smoothed down my bangs. "Laura is really a lovely little girl, down underneath, and I'm sure she will get over it," Mama said. "Some day you'll love her, just the way the rest of us do, and she'll love you, too."

I just sat there, shaking my head and wiping my eyes.

"Laura was jealous, just like this, when we brought Teddy and Rita and Timmy home. Each time she was jealous, but she soon grew to love the new children we adopted." Mama laughed. "Goodness, she was even jealous of baby Alex for a little while."

I still didn't believe that Laura and I would ever be friends. Laura had her mind all made up that she didn't like me. Every day she acted worse, not better.

"Why don't you get back on that airplane and go *away?*" she would say when she passed me on the stairs. She would reach out and pinch me if she could, so I would reach out and pinch *her* whenever I could.

One noonday when Susie and I and Rita and Diane were all up in the treehouse, Laura stood down on the ground and called up. She never came up, because she wasn't a tomboy at all and she didn't climb things. I think she was afraid to climb up that rope ladder.

"Mama says everybody come and wash up for lunch," she shouted.

When I put my head out, she said, "Not you, you old stupid. You might as well stay up there and starve. Nobody likes you!"

Susie put her head out, too, and looked down. "You shouldn't talk like that, Laura. *I* like Elaine, she's my best friend. And Mama and Daddy like Elaine."

Rita zipped out of the treehouse and down that ladder, as fast and sure-footed as a spider. "And *I* like Elaine, too, Laura. And so do all the boys. Do you want a punch in the nose?"

Laura just tossed her head and huffed back to the house.

She was always calling me names, mostly, "Hello, you old stupid." So whenever she passed me, I'd answer right back, "Hello, *bufa.*" She didn't know what a *bufa* was.

Then one day I was out in the yard, playing with Rufus, when Diane and Rita caught a toad over by the toolshed.

"Hey, everybody," Diane called. "We caught a *bufa!*"

"A *bufa?*" Rita said. "Why for do you call him a *bufa?*"

"That's what we call toads in Hawaii," Diane told her.

Laura had been walking by, pushing her favorite doll in her doll buggy. She stopped, listening. Then she came marching over to me, really mad.

"Is that what you're always calling me – a *bufa?*" she said, looking mean enough to bite a nail in half.

"Yeah," I said, sticking out my finger. "You're a *bufa,* a big fat old toad, you are. *Bufa, bufa!*"

"I hate you," she screamed, and she started pulling my hair.

"I hate you, too," I screamed back, and I started pulling her hair twice as hard.

She bit me, then, right on my arm, so I bit her twice on *her* arm. We were both screaming and crying, and Rufus was barking his head off, and all the other kids were shouting for us to stop when Mama ran out and took us apart.

"Girls, girls," she said sorrowfully. "Is that any way for sisters to act?"

"I don't want her to be my sister," Laura sobbed. "I wish that girl would go back on that airplane and go away."

I was crying, too. "I don't want her to be my sister, either."

Mother took us both into the house and cuddled us up beside her on the couch. "Well, you *are* sisters and you'll always be sisters. So the sooner you learn to get along with each other, the sooner you'll learn to enjoy each other. You are both pretty sweet and wonderful girls, you know."

But I didn't think that Laura was anything so sweet and wonderful. I just didn't see how Mama could kiss and hug her the way she did. I loved my new family, but Laura was spoiling all my fun.

We had a good daddy in our family. He and Donny turned the rope so Teddy, Diane and me, and Susie and Laura could see who could jump the fastest.

Wayne Miller, Magnum Photo

Chapter 4. The Surprise

IT WAS the trip to see the doctor that really made things worse between Laura and me — worse than ever before.

Mama told us about the doctor after breakfast.

"Tomorrow," she said, "we all go to the doctor to let him take x-ray pictures of us and make some blood tests."

Laura began to be suspicious right away. "Will that doctor stick a needle in us?"

"Yes, the needle will make a bit of a prick," Mama began.

Laura started to whimper. "Why do we have to get a needle stuck in us?"

"So we won't get dippy-theria," Teddy guessed.

"So our faces won't get locked up," Susie added, "if we step on a rusty nail."

"But we don't *need* diphtheria shots," Donny said, "or lockjaw shots, either. We had that kind this summer already."

"No, it isn't that kind of shot," Mama said. "The doctor just needs to take a tiny bit of blood out with the needle. Then each person's blood can be tested. Then the doctor writes down on some papers that we are all quite healthy in this family. We will take those papers to the judge, so that we can get Elaine and Diane legally adopted to be our very own."

"Oh, I remember," Donny said. "We had to do all that before, when we took Timmy and Alex to the judge to get adopted."

Laura whirled around and pointed her finger right in my face. "That Elaine, *she's* why we all have to go to the doctor!" She was all puckered up like a rain cloud, and her chin quivered. "I always said I wished that girl would go back in the airplane."

Laura kept worrying about those shots all day.

"She just *hates* to have a needle stuck in her," Susie whispered to me.

"Who doesn't?" Rita asked.

"Well, Laura just hates it even more than everybody else," Susie said. "Poor Laura, it bothers her too much."

Laura kept following Mama around. "Do we really have to have those shots?" she kept asking. "*Everybody*, Mama?"

She just couldn't get it out of her mind. I heard her out in the kitchen saying crossly, "That old doctor can't have any of my blood. I need it all myself."

Then I heard Mama comforting her. "Goodness, don't keep thinking about it," Mama said. "Of course you'll get a little prick, but it's over so soon that you'll forget it right away. You remember how it is?"

Susie was standing beside me. "Mama shouldn't have said that," she whispered. "Laura remembers the last time too well, and that's just the trouble."

The next time I saw her she had a sharp pin, and

she was coming toward me with a mean look. I thought she wanted to stick me with it, so I didn't take any chances. I ran out to the treehouse, and climbed up the rope ladder.

"Ha, ha," I teased her. "Can't catch me, and you can't catch a flea." I knew she wasn't a good enough climber to follow me up that rope ladder.

"You *deserve* to get stuck with a pin," Laura shouted. "You're the cause of all our trouble."

There was a can of dirt sitting up in the treehouse, with some dead flowers stuck in it. I just held it out and dumped the whole thing out on top of Laura. I laughed real loud, all the time she was running back to the house.

After Laura was gone and I stopped laughing, I sat there for a while. It didn't seem so funny any more. I found out that it doesn't make you feel good inside after you do something mean to somebody.

Later, I went into the house and upstairs to my room. I saw Laura in her room with all her dolls. She was jabbing each doll with that pin, in their rubber arms. Then she picked them all up and held them.

"Don't cry, babies," she said. "I'm sorry if those nasty old shots hurt." But I noticed that it was Laura who had tears in her eyes, not the dolls.

That night when Mama called us all to dinner everybody came in and sat down except Laura.

"Where's Laura?" Donny asked. "Isn't she eating tonight?"

"Yeah, where's Laura?" Teddy wanted to know.

"Laura?" Timmy said, looking all around.

Little Alex, sitting up in his high chair, pointed a chubby finger at Laura's empty chair. "Oh, oh!" he said.

Just then Laura came in. She had her coat on and her Sunday hat, and she carried her toy suitcase full of doll clothes. Under her other arm, she had her favorite doll, the one she would never let me touch. And on her feet she wore her white Sunday slippers. She never let me touch her slippers, either.

"I'm going to find a better house," Laura said, "where the doctor won't stick little girls with needles." Then she glared at me. "And there aren't any mean old girls getting off airplanes to come live with you."

She had gotten as far as the front door when Mama brought in a platter of sizzling hamburger patties and a bowl of mashed potatoes and put them on the table.

"We're having hamburgers for supper," Donny called. "You'd better stay."

"And mashed potatoes," Teddy said. "Better stay."

"And gravy," Timmy said, as Mama brought that in, too.

"Yum, yum," Little Alex said, rubbing his round tummy.

"And tapioca pudding," Susie said, "for dessert."

"Better stay, Laura," Rita said.

I didn't say anything, because right then I was hoping she *would* go. But everything smelled so good, Laura put her hat and coat away, and climbed up into her chair.

After dinner Laura tried to think of some other way to get out of having those shots the next day. She started rolling her eyes around, and she bent over, holding her stomach as if it hurt.

"I think I'm getting sick," she said, and looked around to see if Mama was getting worried. "I think

Wayne Miller, Magnum Photos

I'll just have to stay home in bed all day tomorrow."

"Maybe some germs ate your healthy up," Susie said.

I gave Laura a real mean look. "Maybe the doctor will stick a getting-well shot in your bottom," I said, and then I laughed. "And then stick the blood test in your arm *too*, ha ha!"

Laura took her hand off her stomach. She straightened up and tried to look really dignified. "I probably just ate too much," she said loudly. "I've still got my healthy."

The next day, right after lunch, Mama washed us all up and gave all the girls clean dresses and the boys clean shirts and jeans. We all put on our Sunday shoes. Diane and I wore our shiny new black patent leather slippers, and Laura wore her new white ones that she had gotten on her last birthday.

When we arrived at the doctor's office, we had to wait while some other people went in first. Laura just sat in a corner, kicking her feet and giving me mean looks, and I kept giving her mean looks right back.

The night before we went to the doctor for our blood tests, Laura kept fussing. She didn't want to get stuck with a needle on my account.

Then the doctor took us in. He smiled and said, "Here comes my big happy family."

We didn't look too happy when he took out his hypodermic needle. He did Teddy first, and Teddy just watched him and didn't even cry. I cried out, just a little, when the needle went in. So did Diane. But Laura was different.

Laura was howling from the minute we walked into the doctor's treatment room. She kept howling as loud as she could, crying that she didn't want to get stuck. Yet the very minute he stuck the needle in, she shut her mouth as tight as a purse. She didn't even let out one little peep.

When he took the needle out, she jumped down from the table. She walked right out of that office without looking at anybody. She held her head up high, just as if she were the queen of the world.

Back at home, Mama told us all to put away our Sunday things and to put our play clothes on again. Timmy and Alex had to go to bed and take their naps because they were younger.

Everybody else, except for me, went outside to

play in a ball game with Donny, out in front of the church.

The house was quiet after they left. The two little boys were downstairs in their bedrooms, going to sleep. Mama was in her bedroom, mending clothes on her sewing machine. Daddy was over at the church, working on his Sunday sermon. And I was all alone upstairs, all alone in the quiet.

I walked down the hall and looked into the room that Laura and Susie and Rita shared. There by Laura's bed were her white Sunday slippers, right where she had kicked them off.

That was funny, because Laura always put her things away. I had to say that for her, she was the neatest child in our family. She never left her things all strewed around the way Diane always did, and the way the rest of us did sometimes. I knew she must have been pretty mad at me to kick off her Sunday shoes and leave them lying there.

As I stood there looking at those shoes, I began to remember something. I remembered what Aunt Lulu had told Diane and me. "If you have an argument with somebody, try stepping into his shoes for a while."

The more I thought about that, the more I wanted to try it.

I just had my socks on, because I had taken off my Sunday shoes already. So I walked right in and slipped my feet into Laura's white shoes.

They fit me just about as well as my own. Laura and I must have feet about the same size, I thought. Well, that was natural, because Laura and I were just about the same age.

I buckled the slipper straps, and then I started walking around in them. I tried to pretend I was Laura.

I thought about how, if *I* were Laura, I would be living very happily in this house, and I would be the oldest girl. Then here comes an airplane from Hawaii with two strange girls on it. These strange girls come home to live with me. One girl is named Elaine, and she is a few months older, so now *she* is the oldest girl in the family.

Then I thought how, if I were Laura, I'd be jealous

of this new girl. Before, Mama had plenty of time to cuddle all three girls, but now she didn't have so much time. "The *new* girls need it most," Mama says. "They haven't had any mama or daddy to cuddle them before."

The more I walked around in Laura's shoes and pretended to be Laura, the more I could see how she must have felt. I knew, then, that *I* would have been jealous of a new, bigger sister, too, if I had been Laura. Why, I'd have probably done just the very same things that Laura did, if I had been Laura!

I thought about how Laura had been made to take an extra shot, all on account of me, just so Daddy could take the papers to the judge and get Diane and me adopted. It is not so bad to get a shot for your own sake, because it will make you well or keep you well. But it is no fun to have to get stuck for the sake of somebody *else*.

And then I remembered how I had dumped that can of dirt right down on Laura's face, and how I laughed at her. I also remembered how I didn't feel good afterward, because I had done something mean.

Suddenly I had a new thought. Maybe Laura wasn't happy because I had made her so jealous. Maybe I made her so mad, calling her names and pinching her back, that she couldn't help doing more mean things. Probably *she* felt bad afterwards, too, and was sorry.

The more I thought about all this, the more I wanted to tell Laura I was sorry I caused her so much trouble. I wanted to tell her that I'd like for us to be friends.

As I ran out through the back door, I saw Laura come scuffing around the side of the church with her head down.

"Hey, Laura," I shouted, running toward her. "I want to tell you something."

She looked up at me, but she saw the white shoes on my feet before she heard me say anything.

"Why, you *Elaine,*" she shouted back. "I'm going to tell Mama you've got my Sunday shoes on. You get those off right now."

The way she was running right at me, I knew I'd better not sit down right there and take them off. I knew that she would be right on top of me before I could start to explain, and then we'd have a real fight.

So I headed as fast as I could for the big tree. I reached it before she did, and scrambled up that rope ladder so fast it left me puffing. When I got up into the treehouse, I looked down. Laura was puffing, too.

"Now listen, Laura, and I'll explain," I said.

"You throw me down those shoes right now," Laura shouted.

"Then I'll get my socks all dirty, walking back to the house," I said. "If you listen to me, I promise I'll walk right back to the house with you. I'll go right upstairs and give you your shoes. And then," I coaxed, "I'll let you play with my new doll if you want."

Laura looked up at me, her head cocked sideways. "You'll let me play with your doll for a whole hour?"

"You can play with her all the rest of today if you want," I told Laura.

"All right," Laura said with her hands on her hips, looking up. "I'm listening."

So then I explained to Laura about what Aunt

Lulu had told me in Hawaii, about walking in somebody else's shoes and pretending you were the other person so you could understand him better.

"So I walked in your shoes," I called down. "And I don't blame you for being mad at me. And I don't blame you for wishing I'd get on an airplane and go away. And I'm sorry that everybody had to have shots on account of Diane and me. I wouldn't have liked that either if I were you." I looked down at her. "And now can I come down?"

"All right," Laura said.

We walked back to the house and up the stairs without saying anything.

When we came into my room, I sat down on the floor to take off the white slippers. But Laura didn't take them. She was looking at my black patent leather Sunday slippers on the floor, where I had dropped them.

"Elaine," she said, "can I try on your black slippers?"

"All right," I said.

She put them on and buckled them. She walked

around and around the room, and then she walked over and looked out of the window for a long time.

When she turned around she smiled, and she looked very pretty and friendly when she smiled.

"I was just pretending, too," she said. "I was just pretending I was a new girl, and I had pretty, new black shoes but I didn't have any family." Her eyes grew wide. "No family in the whole, wide world. And then I came here, and I had a nice family after all." Now the tears started to come into her eyes. "But there was a mean, spiteful girl in that family who told me to get on an airplane and go away."

Laura came and put her arms around me and hugged me. "I think that girl was mean, Elaine," she said, "and I don't think she'd better be mean ever again. Not ever."

"I like you, Laura," I said. "You're nice." I meant it too, because she was nice now.

"I like you too, Elaine," she said. "Put my white shoes back on, and we'll go in my room and have a tea party."

I gave her my new doll, and we went into Laura's

room. She gave me her favorite doll to play with, and she said, "Let's have a lovely tea party for our dolls." So we did.

After a while Susie came up, and she got out her doll, and we invited her to the party, too. Then Diane and Rita came up and looked in the door.

"Dolls," Rita said scornfully. "That's all they ever do is play dolls. Let's go outside and see if we can catch a lizard."

"Okay," Diane said, and they went out.

That night, we went down to supper with our arms around each other, Laura and Susie and me.

"Mama," Laura begged, "can we three all sleep in the big room together, and Diane and Rita take the other room?"

"Well, I don't know," Mama told Laura. "I thought you and Elaine didn't get along so well together."

"That was before," I said. "We get along fine now."

"Yes," Laura said. "We're best friends now, and we always will be. You know, I really liked Elaine from the minute she got off that airplane. I was just jealous for a while, but now I'm all over it."

Mama put her arms around all of us, and hugged us. "I'm proud of both of you. You solved your problems just like grownups." She smiled at us. "Better than some grownups do, I might add."

So we sat down at the table, and I sat between Susie and Laura. We had cupcakes for dessert, and Laura broke hers in half and gave me half. So I gave her the raisin on the top of my cupcake.

I looked proudly at one end of the table at my Mama, and at my Daddy, who was smiling at me down at the other end. I looked at my four brothers of all sizes, Donny and Teddy and Timmy and little Alex. I looked at my sisters, Rita and Diane, who were talking about lizards across the table, and Susie and Laura, who were sitting beside me. Way down inside I felt warm and happy, because now I had my really real family.

And Laura and I stayed best friends ever after that, and we never had any fights or arguments any more. Well, hardly ever.

Laura was the most fun of all, after I got to know her better.